Waiting for the future

Poems by children on poverty and bad housing

Britain is one of the richest countries in the world yet millions of children are living on the breadline, their families unable to afford basic essentials such as food or clothing. They are trapped in homes that are crumbling, dangerous or damp, and lack the security and comfort that we believe is every child's right in modern times.

Poverty and bad housing in Britain

Poverty and bad housing are all around us yet very often hidden from view. The facts are stark. There are 3.5 million children living in poverty, and more than one million living in bad housing.

In this country:

- one in three poor children do not have three meals a day

- one in three poor children lack adequate clothing, in particular shoes and a warm winter coat

- one in 10 children live in bad housing, which is detrimental to their health, leads to them missing out on their education, denies them their privacy, and leaves them with low self-esteem

- one in 12 children are more likely to develop diseases such as bronchitis, TB, or asthma, because of bad housing.

The poems

This collection of poems is written by children of all ages, from all over England. Some of them are suffering the effects of poverty or bad housing. Others voice their frustration at this injustice. All the poems are humbling, compelling and moving.

Bad housing and poverty wreck children's lives – they affect their health, happiness and education. But they don't just suffer in the present; their future life chances are damaged too.

The poems underscore the devastating impact of living in poverty and bad housing. The Government needs to make ending poverty and bad housing for the next generation of children a top priority.

We can't afford to keep our children waiting for a decent future any longer.

Publishing note: in order to maintain authenticity, we have reproduced the children's poems largely as they were presented to Shelter and End Child Poverty, with the original spelling, phrasing and punctuation intact.

Highlighting
the scandal

Shelter and End Child Poverty have collaborated
on this project to enable children to express their
views and feelings as well as to draw attention
to the impact of poverty and bad housing.
We are keen to show that there is hope among
these children that these injustices will change.

We are delighted that the Poet Laureate,
Andrew Motion, has endorsed the project and
very kindly agreed to open the anthology with
his own specially written poem, which you can
read on the following page.

The award-winning musician Ms Dynamite and
Rio Ferdinand, the Premiership and England
International footballer, have also supported our
work. Both have been extremely generous with
their time and support in helping us to highlight
the hidden scandal of bad housing and poverty.

Missing
by Andrew Motion

Whose lives are these, borne on a wing and a prayer,
Thronging the water and earth, the fire and air?

These are the mouths that drank from empty cups;
These are the eyes that no one cared to dry;
These are the tongues that stuck and could not speak;
This was the rain that never swept the sky.

Whose lives are these, borne on a wing and a prayer,
Thronging the water and earth, the fire and air?

These are the feet that stumbled off the road;
These are the hands that planted crops in sand;
These are the arms that gathered only stone;
This was the dust that never turned to land.

Whose lives are these, borne on a wing and a prayer,
Thronging the water and earth, the fire and air?

These are the minds that could not reach the light;
These are the words that blistered in the brain;
These are the thoughts that burned themselves to ash;
This was the flame that never grew again.

Whose lives are these, borne on a wing and a prayer,
Thronging the water and earth, the fire and air?

These are the dreams that ended with the day;
These are the loves that launched through empty space;
These are the hopes that stifled in the heart;
This was the breath that never left a trace.

Children's poems by title

What THEY think of poverty

They think it's only in Victorian England
Dickens and Scrooge and all that
Little kids working down the mines and up chimneys
Head to toe in black and soot

But I know another kind of poverty
That's invisible to them
It's there in the faces of ordinary people
If the rich would just see

We don't have money for expensive school trips or
holidays abroad
Ordinary grub all week and everyday treats is all we
can afford
We'd like to have a car
But skills and money restrict us there too.

It seems the world is run by money
It doesn't buy happiness I know
But without enough of it it's not a jolly show

My parents are good people kind and true
But they cannot afford to take me out to any old 'do'
we choose
because there is not enough money
to pay for lots of new things

And so I cannot spread my wings
The way others do.

Help is at hand
I have a befriender you see
Hayley is her name
And there is no-one better
to show me some of life's pleasures, than she

So if you are 'THEY' then think again
Poverty in England has not yet come to an end.

Darren, age 14

Bad housing

Bad housing can kill,
Bad housing can make you ill.
No time to do your homework,
Only time to do your housework.
To fix the roof where rain comes through,
Then act surprised as if we never knew.
We laugh and smile to make mum feel better,
But the floors in the house get wetter and wetter.
No education, no not no more,
Because we have to dry the floor.
So please help raise a fund to make
poverty history,
So people in bad housing
Can blaze to victory.

Grace, age 9

How to get to Poverty Lane

Go down life's road,
Take a few wrong turnings,
Leave school without taking any exams,
Stop at the off-licence,
Then at junkie junction,
Till you get to the prison,
Drive slowly down Low Pay Drive,
Go right, then wrong,
Through the Bad Housing Estate,
Down Disability Drive
And Cardboard Terrace
Till you run out of luck.
Follow all the signs until you get to the bottom.

Alex, Gemma and Sarah, age 16; and David, Hannah, James,
Mark and Tony, age 15

Three and a half million

Three and a half million of us,
Yet it feels like I'm all alone.
I dread each day, I dread each night.
I dread my life to come.

Three and a half million of us,
Yet it feels like I'm all alone.
I'd like the same toys as everyone else,
And a coat to keep me warm.

Three and a half million of us,
Yet it feels like I'm all alone.
The window shutters swing back and forth
As the creaky floorboards moan.

The gap between rich and poor still grows,
As the rich still grow with greed,
The rich ask for more than they can hold,
While the poor haven't what they need.

He asks for...
A black leather jacket,
Remote control car,
Nike trainers
A fancy electric guitar.

A flashy new phone,
A 20gig MP3
A new mountain bike,
And a flat screen TV.

I ask for...
A kiss from my mother, a hug from my father,
And a pair of shoes without holes.

Three and a half million of us,
Yet it feels like I'm all alone.

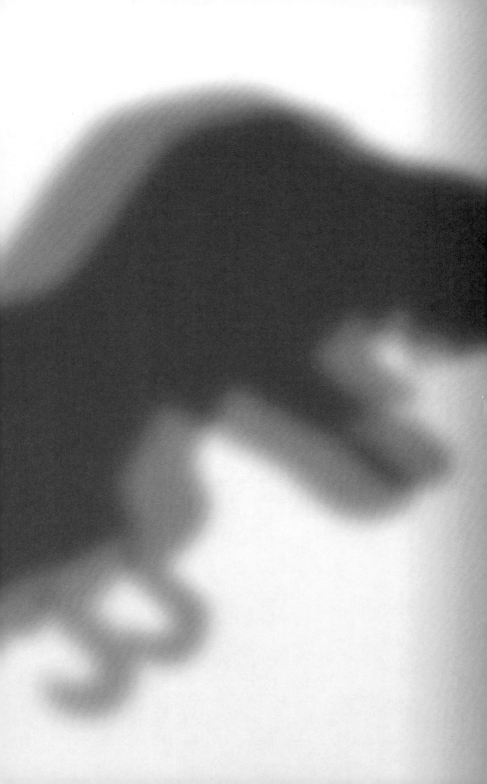

Monster

It growls like an empty tummy,
It scratches like a nitty head,
It's scary as an old damp house,
Its claws are sharp as jealousy.
It bites like the cold,
It camouflages itself like dirt,
It eats people alive,
It grinds their bones.

Poverty kills like an evil monster.
How can we fight it?
How can we destroy it?

Jamie, John Paul, Jordon and Kieran, age 12; and Andrew, age 13   **19**

untitled

My mum has gone for a job
I hope she gets it
I really do
We need it
We haven't got enough money for much food
and drink
I have to go to school in tatty trousers and a torn shirt
My shoes are scruffy and have got holes in.
The water seeps in
We need the money
We really do
I haven't got a jumper or a coat
My mum needs a job
I hope she gets it.

Food, glorious food

Lovely pink milk shakes,
Gorgeous double cheeseburgers,
Salty fish and chips,
Lush chicken nuggets,
Scrumptious mashed potatoes,
Spicy mushroom stir-fry,
Tangy king-prawn curry,
Lip-smacking cream cakes,
Delicious chocolate éclairs,
Runny cream-eggs that melt in your mouth…

We help ourselves and fill our tums
While other children just get the crumbs.

Chelsea, Johnny and Liam, age 11; and Lennox and Simon, age 12   **21**

Such a bad life

All through the night, all through the day.
Nothing but work, no time to play.
Dad is out fishing, catching our food.
When he comes home, he's in such a bad mood.
The baby is screaming, the house is a mess.
We'll be going to bed without supper, I guess?

Ten in a family, such a small house.
All of the cupboards filled with woodlouse.
If only we didn't have such a bad life.
Filled with such sadness, worry and strife.
All through the night, all through the day.
Nothing but work, no time to play.

Rachael, age 12

Living in poverty

Living in Poverty
Always trying

Living in poverty is never wearing something
That someone else has not already worn
Living in poverty is never buying something
That someone else has not already bought
Living in poverty is getting tired of people
Wanting you to be grateful
Living in poverty is checking the coin slot of
Every vending machine as you go by
Living in poverty is hoping your toothache
Will go away
Living in poverty is watching your mum
Making lunch, dropping a piece of meat,
Then looking round to see if anyone saw
Living in poverty is buying a lottery ticket
When you can't afford it

Living in poverty
Still hoping

Shelter

I'm the invisible one
The forgotten one
The one you pretend you can't see
I can't help it
I don't want to be here
I don't want to be me
Do you wonder who I am?
Or don't you care
Am I just a dirty stranger
Someone barely there
Why can't I have
A second chance
A place to call my own
A home?

Freya, age 11

The empty house

I'm lying here upon the floor,
Cold wood presses into my skin,
Looking at the paint-peeled door;
Freezing in a lonely corner.

The single light bulb flickers,
And the room is a darkening pit,
Downstairs my parents bicker,
About what to do with me.

As the wooden walls creak,
An icy wind blows in,
I open my mouth as if to speak,
But all that escapes is a cloud of breath.

My ribs stick out like mountains,
My stomach is as empty as a box,
Tears well out of fountains,
And flood the room to drown me.

They say that this is poverty,
But no one cares about it,
Wouldn't we all like to live like sovereignty?
Though we can never dare to dream.

Matthew, age 14

Help make poverty history

I know what it's like to be homeless,
I was before,
Not any more though,
I'm stuck in cramped housing.
I feel like there's no way out,
Someone offered me drugs,
Obviously I said no,
I'm always cold,
I haven't got many clothes,
When I go to school I always get shouted at
for not doing my
Homework,
It's not my fault though,
I can't it's too noisy where I live,
There's music blaring every day and night.
I just can't concentrate,
I get bullied,
The other day I had my head stamped on,
But nobody does anything about it,
Because they all say 'I'm the kid in a hostel.'

Shannon, age 11

Homeless

Homeless is a bitter, sour feeling.

Not many people have experienced it although unluckily many people have.

Homeless gathers dust like dirty washing that's never been cleaned.

It's like sharp pointy glass always trying to scar you for eternity.

Nobody wants it as it creeps around unnoticed.

Nobody has love for it although they should care for the homeless feeling.

And if they don't all could be lost for the children of the future.

So bring the cold, damp homeless children into the dry warm homes!

Bethany, Natalie, Sachin and Timo, age 10

Homeless: the five Bs

Being homeless feels like you're lonely.

Being homeless looks like a dump.

Being homeless tastes like Sour milk.

Being homeless smells like raw onions.

Being homeless sounds like a bad stomach ache.

History

Everywhere, people stare,
But no-one really seems to care.

Sleeping alone, sleeping rough,
You need to be really tough.

Look at me – what you see?
You really don't want to be me.

Homeless: the five Bs by Mohsin, age 10; *History* by Sarah, age 16

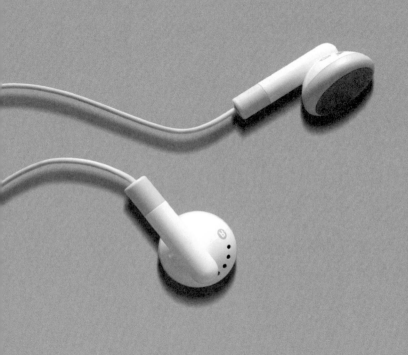

Enjoy yourself

Play on a Game Boy,
Listen to an iPod,
Ride on a mini-motor
Work-out in the gym,
Slide down a chute,
Drive round on a go-kart,
Play on the arcades,
Take a ride on a roller-coaster,
Watch your favourite football team,
Watch TV,
Ride a BMX,
Go out for a family meal,
Go shopping for shoes –
Go on, enjoy yourself.

But never forget that 3.5 million
Children live in poverty in Britain.

Chelsea, Johnny and Liam, age 11; and Simon, age 12

I dreamed

I dreamed there was a door
it was bright as the sun.
Once there was a green door
with nothing but scratches.

I dreamed there was a room
with the most amazing carpet I could feel
the softness of it reached my foot.
Once there was a wood floor
it would feel rusty and never soft.

I dreamed there was a bedroom
it was so warm I couldn't
feel even a blow of air, reach
me, once there was a breeze
of cold air like you were outside and snowing.

I dreamed there was an amazing
kitchen with pine cupboards
and handles
once there were scratched
cupboards and white handles

Nowhere, no-one

I was walking down the street,
there were kids playing in big gardens,
the smell of food coming out of big houses.

People were saying
'EEW, look at him'
and some people called me a tramp.

People were looking at me and frowning,
people who wouldn't stop staring at me,
and other people turning away quickly.

I could feel the wet walls
and the soggy muddy grass
and the pouring rain falling to my toes.

Kayleigh, age 10

Bad housing,
a child's thoughts

So cold and empty

Hopeless, hungry and frustrated

Ever looking over my shoulder

Longing for a decent home

Tired of poverty and overcrowding

Endless sadness in my heart

Relief, will it come?

Waiting

Hungry kids racking out the bins,
Scruffy little children, eating out of tins,
This freezing flat's not much of a home,
Shivering with cold, trying to get warm,
Waiting for some money, waiting for a loan,
Waiting for the future – Home Alone…

Bad housing, a child's thoughts by Robert, age 12;
Waiting by Daniel, Dean, Ross and Wayne, age 14;
and Rebecca, age 13

Hunger

Staring at the plate and there's
nothing in front of me
hunger hunger

Walking in the street and my
Stomach is rumbling
Hunger hunger

Staring in my purse and there's no
Money to get anything
Hunger hunger

I looked in the cupboards there's
Nothing for me to eat
Hunger hunger

My hungry tummy is rumbling rumbling.

Home less

Being homeless feels like being scared

Being homeless sounds like cars whizzing past.

Being home less tastes like rotten Bread

Being home less looks like sunless, gloomy and dark like midnight.

Being homeless smells like a dog dead

Will people be homeless in 2020?

James, age 11

My battle against poverty

I pressed my hand against the frosted glass,
And looked out to see,
The girl who lived across the road.
She came out of her home,
It had windows that weren't smashed,
With two cars parked in the yard,
It looked like a fantasy home.

How I longed for a house like that,
How I wished to be just like her,
With fresh clothes every day,
A bedroom all to myself,
A warm house,
And much more.

She didn't have to worry,
About any loan sharks coming to threaten her.
She wasn't teased everyday,
She had everything I didn't.

Was it because she was better than me,
Or was it simply because I was battling against,
Cruel and Ruthless POVERTY!!!

Sughita, age 12

Unlucky

The ammonia-stink of an old mattress,
The crunch of stale, dry bread,
The echo of your breath,
An empty fridge,
The screeching of your hungry baby sister,
The taste of cold, damp air,
The mud-stuck, warm smell of yesterday's track-suit,
The same food every day,
The mouth-watering smell of a restaurant,
Cobwebs hanging from the ceiling,
The sound of your life ticking away.
How unlucky is that ?

Daniel, Dean, Ross and Wayne, age 14; and Rebecca, age 13

End child poverty

I wake in the morning,
A brand new day,
Is that a good thing?
It's hard to say.

A dark, cramped bedroom,
The windows are grey,
Cold porridge for breakfast,
Nowhere to play.

I walk to the park,
With my mum and six brothers,
To hide from the bailiffs,
One man and some others.

I hear mother crying,
In her bedroom at night,
I go in and tell her,
That it's all right.

I know it won't be,
And so does she,
But hearing those words,
Makes you think it will be.

I cry as well,
This is all down to me,
People leave gifts and say
'You can have them for free.'

I wish we had money,
Like other kids have,
To buy some clean clothes,
Instead of these rags.

I know we're not rich,
Like some people are,
We don't have a big house,
Or a nice shiny car.

But because we've no money,
People think we're worthless,
I just want a decent life,
Like everyone else.

Safiyyah, age 12

untitled

I feel cold and sad
I haven't got any heating
My home is cold and damp
Water runs down the wall and
Makes my bed wet
My fingers draw on the window
It's like fog
I try to pull the cover over me to get warm
But it doesn't work
I'm cold and sad

Luke, age 9

So sad to see

Homelessness looks like a revolving hurricane broke down your house.

It sounds like a crashing wave coming past.

It smells like a burning battlement.

It tastes like disgusting smelly bins.

It almost feels like we're going to lose our lives very soon.

Will it change, hopefully it might in the future?

I wish…

I wish I had more money,
I wish I had more clothes,
I wish I had new trainers,
I wish… I wish…
I wish I lived in a house,
I wish I had an education,
I wish I had better food,
I wish… I wish…
I wish my Dad had a car,
I wish my mum had a job,
I wish we could pay the rent,
I wish… I wish…
And now you've heard me talk, about my hopes
And dreams, and I hope you understand, you have
The things we need. And now just imagine, what
Life is like for us, and what we have today, is just
Not enough.

Timi, age 12

What it is like to be homeless...

I know I have been there
Walking away from a dark and blackened house,
With only the clothes on my back.
Days went with mum and dad waiting for the
homeless unit.
The sadness of losing my dogs.
My brothers and sisters being farmed out
to friends and
Family, and the joy at last of being together
With the people I love.

Caring
Homeless
Isolated
Left alone
Down and out
Remissed
Evicted
Nomadic

Hannah, age 11

The empty plate

Empty plate is the hunger in front of me
Empty, Empty,
My stomach is rumbling deep inside of me
Rumbling, Rumbling
The cupboard in front of me is
Empty, Empty,
There's nothing for breakfast or even for
Dinner
Nothing, Nothing,
My stomach is still rumbling deep inside
Of me
Rumbling, Rumbling.

Sarah, age 10

There is no place like home

Gary's home is like stepping into a freezer

Stephanie's home is as cosy as a cushion of clouds

The thought of Gary going home to his wintry home
makes him feel inconsolable,

But Stephanie skips to her summery home
as lightly as a feather.

Gary's home is as lonely as a graveyard

Stephanie's home is as cheerful as Santa,

Gary swims in his deep dark puddle of doubts,
alone in his room.

Stephanie chatters happily with her bright
and bubbly friends.

As Gary's stomach rumbles like a devastating earthquake

Stephanie feasts upon a pile of scrumptious, tasty and delicious food.

Who would you like to be?

Where would you rather live?

Who should Gary talk to?

Bethany, Felicity, Nathan, Romessa and Tasneen, age 10; and Hashim, age 11

Do you dream of a perfect home?

I dreamt there was a slated roof,
And the colours were spread like an eagle,
The door was opened and it was white,
The wooden sign had carved in it
'This little cottage is gifted'
Once there was a wooden door,
With no colour seen in it.

I dreamed there was a sort of cloakroom,
On my right there were hooks for coats,
On my left were stairs,
In front, a kitchen.
Once there was a horrible hallway,
With cracks and spaces in the walls,
There were only tiny hooks and looking forward,
A messy living room.

I dreamed there was a kitchen made of stone,
An old but beautiful one,
An oven and cooker was in too,
The heat was refreshing and the cupboards,
Filled with a sweet centred smell.
Once there was a cramped kitchen,
With only a fire and a cooker,
And a table,
It was dirty and I was disgusted.

I dreamed there was my room,
Tidy and clean, a bit small but nice,
In the garden were the flowers,
Poppies were beside my feet,
I felt as if it were a new life.
Once there were no garden,
And the bedroom was shared
And it was a flat squashed untidy.

Emma, age 10

Is it?

Miss is always shouting –
It's just not fair.

I always get the blame –
It's just not fair.

They say I'm gay –
It's just not fair.

Sir makes us work –
It's just not fair.

I've hurt me hand –
It's just not fair.

I wish I was bigger –
It's just not fair.

She's pinched me scissors –
It's just not fair.

This school's too noisy –
It's just not fair.

Me girlfriend's dumped us –
It's just not fair.

I've run out of tabs –
It's just not fair.

I'm not very brainy –
It's just not fair.

Dads who hit their kids –
It's just not fair.

Terrorist bombs –
It's just not fair.

So much unkindness –
It's just not fair.

Too much hunger –
It's just not fair.

Kids who live in poverty
It's just not fair.

It's just not fair.

Lee and Stephen T, age 14;
and Colin, Jamie, Kyle and Stephen W, age 13

Children
in poverty

Home is meant to mean your own personal space.
Not being cramped up.
Home is meant to mean looking forward to coming home.
Not thinking of an excuse not to come home.
Home is meant to be around your family.
Not being shouted at and worried.
Home is meant to be a safe place to live.
Not weird people coming in demanding money.
Home is meant to be a fun happy place to live.
Not a cold sad place.
Home is meant to have friends over.
Not being too ashamed to invite anyone over.
Home is meant to be home.
So let's make it home for the children that
Have to put up with that.

Poverty

Day in day out
I just want to break out
So many people have lied
I just can't feel a good vibe
So many things going on in my head
All I want is a nice warm bed
Why oh why am I so poor?
A nice warm bed, come on people is that so much
to ask for?
I'd love to see you live one day as me
I'll be laughing Ha Ha Hee Hee
I wish I was in a better mood
I wish I had some decent food

So now you have just seen a day in the life of me.

O'Shaya, age 12

A poem about poverty

Poor and unwealthy
Overlooked by the rich
Vulnerable and weak
Empty and heartbroken
Ravenous and homeless
Thirsty and hungry
Young and helpless

Hungry

I could smell the barbeque.
I could hear the children laughing,
the dog barking.

I turned away,
hungry for food,
hungry for laughter.

untitled

School's out and I'm going home
There will be no tea
I feel really really hungry
It's the same day after day
My mum had to work night shift night after night
She doesn't have much money to buy me food
and drinks,
Or to keep me warm.
I don't have many clothes
And my shoes are scruffy.
I go to bed hungry and cold
Nobody is home.

I'm alone!!!

There is life everywhere around me,
Everything feels dead!

There is talking I can hear it,
But the atmosphere's silent!

I'm in the same room as them,
They hardly know I exist!!!

No-one is smoking,
But I'm choking anyway!

It's not raining,
But my face is getting wet!

There are people in this room,
But I'm soooo alone – please help
Me!!

Alexandra, age 11

untitled

I know I will go home hungry
I will go to bed cold
I know the next day I will miss the school trip
We don't have enough money for uniform
Every day is the same
Every day I get picked on
Sometimes I wish I were a leaf
So I could just fly away.

Joe, age 8

Children in poverty

S – s is for safety and security,
so the children will be happy.

H – h is for bad housing,
which children shouldn't have.

E – e is for eating, children should
eat three times a day.

L – l is for lonely, children should
spend time with family and friends.

T – t is for tough, so children
should exercise.

E – e is for education,
so children can get a job.

R – r is for respect, children should
be respected as well as others.

Catch
the dream

When you look back in life
And remember all the strife
Think it's behind in the past.

But you open your eyes
And all you see is tears
The cogs click into place
The path before your face
Catch the dream!

You're running through the mess
And then you lose your stress
Left there smothered
Are all of the others.
Lives destroyed
By the dark and sweeping cloud
The thunder clear and loud.

Luke, age 13

No poor people

If there were no poor people in the future
It would just be rich people
They would be happy
And they would have a big house
And they will have money
And they will be so happy

Why me?

Why am I so different?
Why do I have no friends?
Why is my house cold and damp?
Why do I never stay in one place?

Why me?

The bakery

I was sitting on a bench
with the smell of the bakery,
I could see children
running out of the shop with sweets
and the children's parents
with bread and cakes.

Will anyone buy treats for me?
Will a parent ever hold my hand?
Will I ever taste what I can smell?

untitled

I'm at school,
Being laughed at again,
My clothes are not the same,
I feel left out and sad inside,
I'm so alone and teased at school,
I really don't want to be different.

The bakery by Hayley, age 10; *Untitled* by Elise, age 8

My senses

I see people smirk as I walk into the classroom.
I see them point and whisper as I go past.

I hear them call me names and laugh in my face.
I hear rumours about me circulate like bees.

I feel the embarrassment of having to turn down yet
another school trip.
I feel the other kid's comments peck at me like
vultures.

I taste the school dinner that I went through such
humiliation to get.
I taste all the food but still feel so empty inside.

I smell the damp walls of our house.
I smell the stench of cigarettes next door.

Some people think that just because I can't afford all
the things they can,
It makes me less of a person than everyone else.
And if you are one of those people,
It makes you the poorest person in the world.

A rumbling echo

I came home and there's nothing to
Cook.
Mum's not home and my belly's
Rumbling.

Rumbling,
My belly's rumbling.
Rumbling.

My mum called and she's coming home
Late.
My stomach is empty, I'm so hungry.

Rumbling,
My belly's rumbling
Rumbling.

All I'm doing is watching TV
There are people eating on my
Favourite channel.

Rumbling,
My belly's rumbling
Rumbling.

I'm hungry and my belly is...
Rumbling.

Inas, age 10

Empty stomach

Empty stomach grumbling.
Empty empty.
No food on the cooker
To satisfy me after
School-empty empty
No mum asking for help
In the kitchen-empty
Empty
No snacks to snack on-
Empty empty
Nothing to eat-empty
Empty.
Grumbly stomach feeling
Empty empty.

Angelika, age 10

Being homeless

Being
    homeless
        feels
            lonely.
Being
    homeless
        smells
            of
                smelly
                    junk.

Being
    homeless
        sounds
            like a
                car
                    siren.
Being
    homeless
        tastes
            like
                garlic
                    and
                        sprouts.

The clothes don't fit

I've been dreading this day,
It had to come soon.
In the back of my mind,
The 1st of June.

The plain grey dress,
It hardly fits.
Patches of dirt,
And torn into bits.

The kids all looked,
They laughed and stared.
I felt so angry,
Yet really scared.

My hair was a mess,
All strewn everywhere.
My parents, I thought,
Didn't even care.

Look at them all,
They must think I'm strange.
I'll face the fact,
My life will never change.

Toni, age 12

If only

We could have two swimming pools,
Wear lots of expensive jewels,
I could fly among the stars,
Take a trip to far-off Mars –
Oh, if only my Dad had a job!

I would drink ice-cold milk shakes,
Every day eat chocolate cakes,
Spend all day on theme-park slides
And chocolate roller-coaster rides –
Oh, if only my Dad had a job!

I would ride a motor-bike,
I'd do anything I like,
I would fly an aeroplane,
And swim in baths of pink champagne –
Oh, if only my Dad had a job!

I would wear a gorgeous gown,
On my head a golden crown,
I would dress in Barbie pink,
Wear a fur coat made of mink,
But my Dad he just can't find a job,
No, my Dad he just can't find a job.

Jamie and Stephen W, age 13; and Stephen T, age 14

23rd of July,
15,000,005

I can't believe that in the year 2005,
when I was younger,
there was so much poverty.
But now the world has no poverty.
The world looks more beautiful than 14,998,000
years ago
and it is covered with flowers.

I can't live there

Damp with rats carrying germs,
I wish I wasn't there.
Leaking roofs, unstable floors, I hate,
to be there.
Teenagers telling me things I shouldn't know,
I wish I was somewhere else, somewhere,
Where I can live.
Please help me Mr Government,
I beg you, I plea.

23rd of July, 15,000,005 by Lucas, age 8;
I can't live there by Edmund, age 8

In your shoes

My peers preaching,
Of the goods they will receive.
But me…
All hope is lost,
As I cannot expect,
Many any presents…

I must pretend
I have the wealth,
To afford the latest craze.
I wish, I wish, I wish,
I could be in someone else's shoes.

Their Nike shoes…

Mummy and me

So mummy,
What have we got to get today?
I will tell you on the way.
Right, we need...
Half a pound of damp walls
A kilogram of ruined lives
Five litres of tears
Five hundred grams of cardboard boxes
One tatty old teddy
Twenty packets of sad faces
Three rotten blankets
Ten bags of sleepless nights
Seven buckets of bruises
Fifteen loaves of broken homes
Eight tins of broken bones
Seventeen boxes of unloved hearts
A bottle of rotten luck
3.5 million kids lives neglected
3.5 million lives, are they worth living?

Jess, Lauren and Zoe, age 14

The rich kid

I'm a rich kid,
I'm a star.
When I'm 18,
I'll have a car.
Always with lots of money,
Thinking it's all so very funny.

Then I saw kids who were poor,
I noticed they needed so much more.
The conditions so horrible and bad,
This made me sad and slightly mad.

Knowing I'm greedy,
Donating money to the needy.
Helping people to have a home,
Making sure they will never be alone.

Mark, age 11

FINE
PEARLS
DIAMONDS
&
COLOURED
GEMS

untitled

Cold
Hungry
Ill
Lonely
Danger
Reality
Empty Inside
No fun

Insecure
Needy

Poverty
On their own
Vulnerable
Everywhere
Ridiculous
Teased
Y does this happen?

Jessica, age 11

The solution

What can we do to help the poor?

Not faraway supermarkets
but near, healthy supermarkets,
not lack of money
but children's lives that are sunny,
not dying younger,
not dying of hunger
but killing of hunger.

We all deserve the same
of everything!

Empty pockets

In this clothes shop
I smell of wet dogs.
My sore cut feet
are hurting as I nervously
walk along the cold
hard floor
past well-dressed people
all fashionable,
while I wear
cut, ripped and dirty
clothes.
People buy things which
I would love to have.
They have a smile which
I would love to have.

Jessica, age 10

Seasons

Spring

The house is bare with not much light,
The day is near but it feels like night,
All I have is just a flimsy blanket,
But still I don't complain.

Summer

The months go on with not much hope,
With so much work I cannot cope,
I want to go outside and play
But still I don't complain.

Autumn

The trees turn orange my favourite colour,
But I stay indoors and help my mother,
When really I wish to walk alone,
But still I don't complain.

Winter

Bitter chill and frosty nose,
I'm so cold in my thin clothes,
Christmas comes and Christmas goes,
But still I don't complain.

Here I am

Here I am walking down my road,
Not wanting to go home.

Thinking to myself why can't I be like other
Children healthy, wealthy, and have a good quantity
of friends.

Every day I reflect on how my life has been unfolding,
But all the memories have been cold and frightening.

I live in an old temporary house with my mum
and sister,
And it's unhygienic and mouldy.

Before I go to bed on the damp floor
with only a sheet to
Cover me,
I pray that I could be like other children healthy,
wealthy, and
Have a good quantity of friends.

Philip, age 12

Homeless

Jack Frost is running about
Hitting them hard
As poverty did.
A bed of stone
In their broken-down home
Shutters slamming.
A blanket
And their soul
Rattling inside their head
As empty as a hole

I can't

I touch the price tag,
stroke the shoes,
then shake my head.

I touch the price tag,
stroke the jacket,
then shake my head.

I touch my pocket,
stroke the empty pouch,
then shake my head.

Homeless by Tom, age 14; *I can't* by Paige, age 10

Excuses

Everyone agrees we should try to end Child Poverty.
Don't they?

But the greedy man says,
'when I've finished me chips,'

And the lazy teenager says,
'hold on, I'm still in bed,'

And the busy man says,
'sorry mate, I'm in a rush, got to fly,'

And the angry old man says,
'piss off – do you think I care?'

And the fashion model says,
'I can't do that, I might break a nail,'

And the journalist says,
'it's not exciting enough to put in the paper,'

And the computer-geek says,
'yeah, whatever, when I finish this level,'

And the worried woman says,
'stop harassing me, you bully,'

And the thief says,
'never mind that – give me your wallet'

And the dopehead says,
'not interested man – got a spliff?'

And the school-kid says,
'what's in it for me? What do I get out of it?'

But everyone agrees we should try to end Child
Poverty. Don't they?

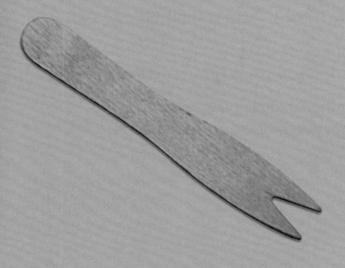

Why poverty?

I thought home was meant to be cheerful
My home isn't that. My home is tearful.
Why is my home different?

I thought home was meant to bring heat and comfort
My home isn't that. My home is cold and brings
Discomfort.
Why is my home different?

I thought homes were meant to be full of family.
My home isn't that. My family. Are never there.
Why am I different?

I thought family provide food to fill my tummy.
We're not that. I'm always hungry.
Why? Why? Why?

Homes are meant to bring happiness.
Why does mine bring sadness?

Why do I have to be different?
Why can't I be like everyone else?
Why do I have to live in poverty?

Ignored

I walked into the classroom,
Smelling in my rags.
The other children just stared and whispered.
They didn't know, they didn't care.
People like me are just kept in the closet.
Nearly everyone pretends we don't exist.
Mum couldn't do a thing about it, our situation.
However hard she tried, nothing was ever done.
We were there.
There forever.

Chelsea, age 12

Britain 2005

Poor children don't get enough food
This is Britain 2005

Poor children can't go on school trips
This is Britain 2005

Poor children don't get toys
This is Britain 2005

Poor children miss out on after-school activities
This is Britain 2005

Poor children miss 25% of school
This is Britain 2005

Poor children catch disease from bad housing
This is Britain 2005

Poor children have no privacy in their own homes
This is Britain 2005

Let's change it for Britain 2006

Rebecca, age 10

untitled

Poor
Old
Vicious
England
Rejects
The
Young.

Safe
Houses
Express
Love
To
Every
Resident.

Andrew, Gemma and Laura, age 15

Thank you

We would like to thank the following schools, advice projects and after-school clubs, all of which have taken part in creating *Waiting for the future*. We would also like to thank all the children who contributed poems, and the arts projects and poets who facilitated the poetry-writing in some of the schools. This anthology is a selection of the many poems we received. Without the enthusiasm and commitment of all of those involved, this project would not have been possible.

Participating schools and projects:

Alsop High School, Campion City Learning Centre, Liverpool
Brackenedge Primary School, Leeds
Cutteslowe Primary School, Oxford
Diss High School, Norfolk
Eltham Green School, Greenwich, London
Fun In Action, Brighton
Grange Park Primary School, Sunderland, Tyne and Wear
Graveney School, Tooting, London
Hillcrest Primary School, Leeds
Holy Name Primary School, Moss Side, Manchester
Moorside Community Primary School, Newcastle upon Tyne
Northbridge House High School, Camden, London
Norton Hill School, Midsomer Norton, Bath
Oxford Community School, Oxford
Runaways Education Project, Hebden Bridge, Yorkshire
St Thomas More Secondary School, Haringey, London
Stockton Wood Junior School, Speke, Liverpool
Tavistock Community School, Tavistock, Devon
The Meadows School, Spennymoor, County Durham
Tracker Project, space@brackenedge, Leeds
Word Play Group, Leeds

Facilitating arts projects and poets:

Devon Arts in School Initiative
New Writing North, Newcastle
Windows Project, Liverpool

Maureen Almond
Rosanne Angwin
Andy Croft
John Hughes
Curtis Wall